Better Homes and Gardens®

CRAZY CREATURES

Hi! My name is Max. I have some great projects to show you—and they're all about crazy creatures! We're going to have lots of fun making them together.

© Copyright 1988 by Meredith Corporation, Des Moines, Iowa.
All Rights Reserved. Printed in the United States of America.
First Edition. Fifth Printing, 1990.
Library of Congress Catalog Card Number: 90-169293
ISBN: 0-696-01897-7 (hard cover)
ISBN: 0-696-01810-1 (trade paperback)
MAX THE DRAGON™ and MAX™ and other characters in this book are trademarks and copyrighted
characters of Meredith Corporation, and their use by others is strictly prohibited.

Inside You'll Find...

Discover the zoo animals and count them, too.

Crazy Zoo Creatures

Max and his best friend, Elliot, are having fun at the zoo.
They like to walk around and look at all the wild animals.

Can you help Max count
the animals?
- 1 elephant
- 2 lions
- 3 rhinoceroses
- 4 giraffes
- 5 turtles
- 6 birds

Did you know...

● A giraffe once was called a camelopard. Can you guess why? It's because a giraffe looks like a mixture of two other animals—a camel and a leopard.

● A toucan (TOO-can) is a bird with a very long and colorful beak.

In fact, its beak is as long as its body! A toucan uses it like a knife to slice through its food.

● A turtle can't just walk away from its shell. The shell is part of the turtle's body, just like your back is part of your body.

5

Little fingers use ink to make fast artwork.

Thumbprint Critters

If you're all thumbs when it comes to drawing, then you'll love making these Thumbprint Critters.

What you'll need...

- Ink stamp pad, tempera paints, or chocolate syrup
- Paper
- Markers, colored pencils, or crayons

1 Press your thumb or fingertip onto an ink stamp pad. Press the inked thumb onto a piece of paper (see photo). This will leave your thumbprint on the paper. Make as many prints on the paper as you like.

2 Let the prints dry. Draw faces, legs, and other features on your critters with markers (see photo).

I like using chocolate syrup so I can lick my fingers!

CHOCO SYRUP

6

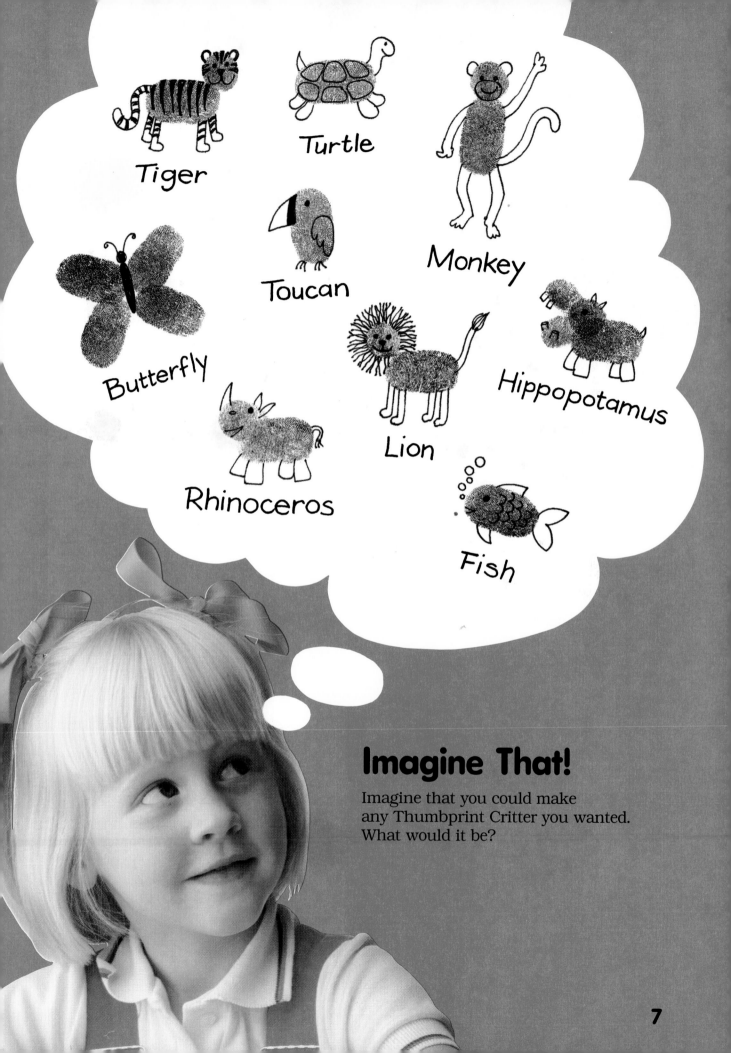

Tiger

Turtle

Monkey

Butterfly

Toucan

Hippopotamus

Rhinoceros

Lion

Fish

Imagine That!

Imagine that you could make
any Thumbprint Critter you wanted.
What would it be?

Bread dough becomes a herd of delicious snacks.

Eat-'Em-Up Animals

Did you know you can make a zoo in your kitchen? Shape bread dough into creatures and bake them in the oven.

What you'll need...

● Foil
● Baking sheet
● Tape
● Shortening

● Frozen bread dough, thawed, or one 11-ounce package refrigerated French bread dough

● Creature Features (see tip on page 9)
● 1 beaten egg
● 1 tablespoon water

1 Tear a piece of foil the size of your baking sheet. Tape foil to the counter. Lightly grease foil. Using the bread dough like clay, make animal shapes on the foil (see photo). Use Creature Features to decorate animals.

2 Remove the tape from the foil. Carefully lift the foil and dough onto the baking sheet.
   Brush dough with a mixture of egg and water (see photo).

MUNCH!
MUNCH!

MAX
THE
COOK

3 With adult help, bake dough in a 375° oven about 15 minutes or till golden brown.
   Use hot pads to remove the baking sheet from the oven. With a pancake turner, lift the hot dough animals off the foil and onto a wire rack. Let the dough animals cool.

Creature Features

Decorate your dough animals with snipped raisins, currants, dried fruit bits, or nuts. These foods make great eyes, noses, or even belly buttons!

Craft a snake by cutting a spiral out of paper.

Slithering Snakes

Snakes are fun to play with—when they're made with paper.

What you'll need...

- Construction paper or paper plate
- Scissors
- Crayons or markers
- Tape
- 2-inch piece of pipe cleaner or crinkle ribbon

1 Draw a spiral on the paper to resemble a coiled snake. Starting at the outside edge, cut along the line (see photo). Throw away any scraps of paper.

2 Color the paper to make it look like a snake.

3 Make a tongue by taping the pipe cleaner to the head of the snake. Be sure to tape the tongue on the underside of the head (see photo).

Now lift the snake by its tongue and watch it slither!

Sparkle Snakes

How about making a snake that sparkles with glitter? It's easy. After you cut out your snake, squeeze glue onto the paper. Sprinkle colorful glitter over the glue and let it dry.

11

Mother Nature made spiders special. Here's how.

Spiders, Spiders Everywhere

Max and his friend, Elliot, like spiders. They know it's OK to look, but not to touch them. How many spiders can you find?

Look! Max sees hidden letters in the spiderweb. Can you see them, too? What do the letters spell?

Did you know...

● Spiders are not insects. Insects have six legs and spiders have eight. Spiders are called arachnids (uh-RACK-nids). Can you say that?

● Spiders can run fast. You could run fast, too, if you had eight legs!

● Spiders spin webs to live in and to catch food. But did you know that spiders can get caught in their own sticky webs? This doesn't usually happen, though. Spiders spin some "safe" threads into their webs. They know they won't stick to these.

● Some spiders hang on to the threads they spin and are blown through the air by the wind.

● In the fall, they spin a little ball of spider silk that looks like cotton candy. These spider cocoons are called fairy lamps.

● A water spider spins a silky bag underwater. It fills the bag with air bubbles from the surface and then lives inside the bag.

Turn the page to see how to make your own spider.

13

A nut cup and pipe cleaners become a fuzzy-legged spider.

Silly Pet Spider

The best spider to have for a pet is the kind you make.

What you'll need...

- Spider Faces
  (see tip on page 15)
- Paper nut cup or
  egg carton cup
- Pencil
- Eight 3-inch pieces
  of pipe cleaner or
  eight twist ties

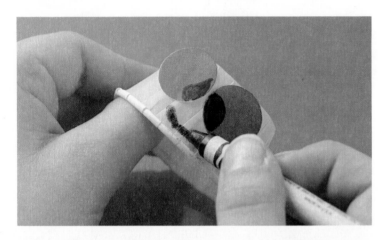

1 Decorate the nut cup to make it look like the face of a spider.

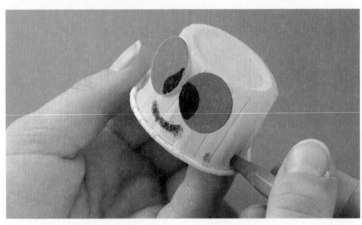

2 With adult help, using the tip of a pencil, poke 8 holes around the bottom edge of the nut cup.

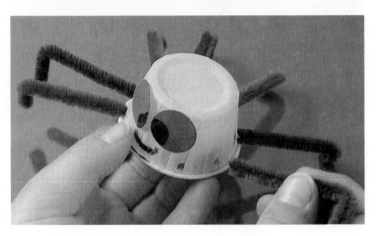

3 To make the spider's legs, insert pipe cleaners into the pencil holes.

Spider Faces

Your Silly Pet Spider can have any face you like. Use crayons or markers to draw the eyes and mouth. Use adhesive stickers for the eyes, or glue on cereal or raisins. You can even give your spider a funny hat by gluing on fluffy cotton balls or tiny marshmallows.

An easy string-and-glue project.

Spin a Spiderweb

Pretend you're a spider. You can make your own web using string and glue.

What you'll need...

- Tape
- Waxed paper
- White crafts glue

- Six 9-inch pieces of medium-weight cotton twine

- Three 12-inch pieces of medium-weight cotton twine

1 Tape a piece of waxed paper to the counter. Squeeze a glob of glue onto the waxed paper.

Tape a second piece of waxed paper to the counter for the web. Dip a 9-inch piece of twine into the glue. Pull the twine through your first finger and thumb to remove extra glue (see photo). Wipe off excess glue.

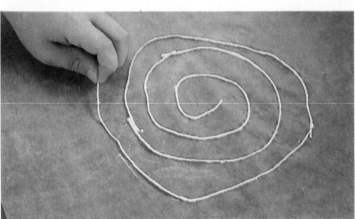

2 To start the web, lay one end of the twine in the center of the second piece of waxed paper. Working outward from the center, lay down twine.

To continue, dip the rest of the 9-inch pieces of twine into the glue and lay them down (see photo). Be sure to overlap the ends of the twine.

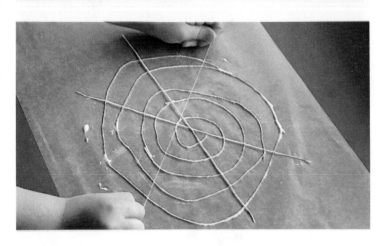

3 Dip one of the 12-inch pieces of twine into the glue. Take off extra glue. Lay the long piece of twine across the web in a spoke design (see photo). Repeat with remaining twine.

Let dry for at least 4 hours. Carefully peel the web off the waxed paper.

Making Silly Spiders

Now that you've spun a web, make a spider to hang on it.

Make the pink spider using crinkle ribbon for legs and a coding label for the body. Tape or glue legs to the body. Use a marker to draw on the eyes.

Make the red spider by twisting four pieces of pipe cleaner together. Then glue buttons on for the eyes.

The black spider belongs to Max. He bought it at the store.

A special garden with hidden surprises.

Sneak-a-Peek Garden

One morning, Max was working in his garden. He was surprised to find five crazy creatures hidden in the garden. Can you find them, too?

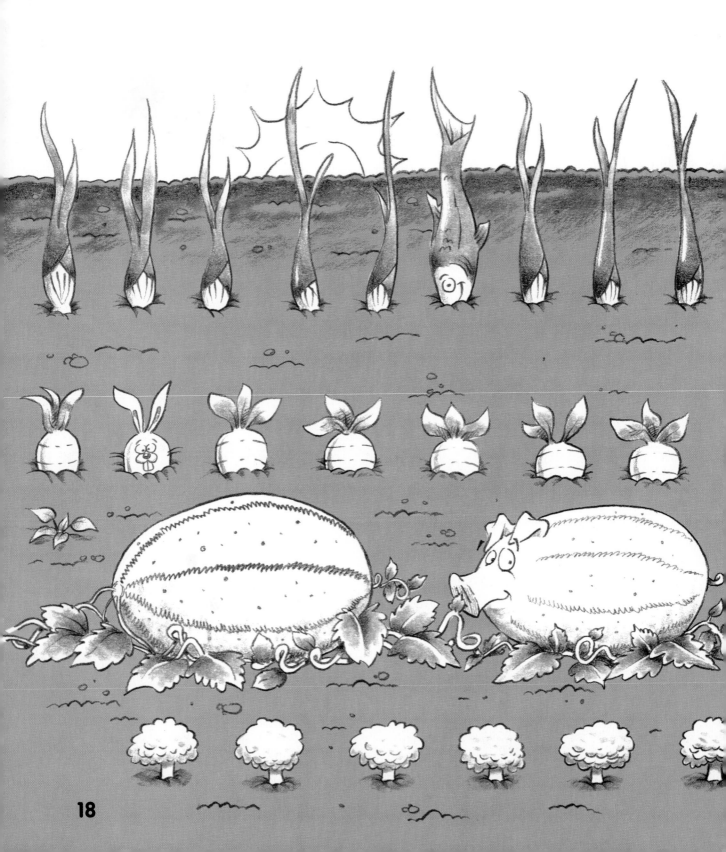

Garden-Patch Chatter

Max's favorite vegetable is a carrot. He thinks it makes his tail big and strong. Did you know that vegetables and fruits are good for you? Max does. He eats vegetables and fruits every day. What is your favorite vegetable? Do you have a favorite fruit? What else do you see in the garden?

Sprout a leafy friend from a sweet potato.

Sweet-Potato Partners

Every sweet potato is a crazy creature waiting to sprout leafy hair. Add a funny face and you've got your own spud buddy.

What you'll need...

- 3 toothpicks
- Sweet potato
- Jar or glass
- Face decorations
- Water

1 Stick toothpicks in the potato (read tip on opposite page). The toothpicks should be about halfway down the potato and equal distance from each other. Decorate your potato to make it look like a crazy creature (see photo).

2 Fill about half of the jar with water. Place your sweet potato into jar (see photo). If necessary, pour in more water to almost fill jar.

Put your potato partner near a sunny window.

Make a Funny Face

Before you stick toothpicks into your sweet potato, take a good look at it. Do you see small purple shoots starting to grow at one end? That's the end of the sweet potato that will sprout leafy hair. Be sure to put the other end into the water.

You don't need special materials to make a potato face. Just use markers or paper cutouts. Or try toothpicks, coding labels, marshmallows, golf tees, plastic foam cups, corks, modeling clay, sunglasses, pipe cleaners, or ribbon.

In a few days, your sweet potato will grow roots in the water.
Within a week, you should be able to see leaves growing on top.

Food from the garden makes good-tasting creatures to snack on.

Crunchy Creatures

For these crazy creatures, radishes can be heads, zucchini can be bodies, and pickles can be noses. Use our creatures below for ideas, or make up your own.

What you'll need... ● Toothpicks ● Carrot and zucchini, cut into chunks ● Radishes ● Sliced almonds ● Cream cheese or peanut butter ● Round toasted oat cereal ● Raisins ● Chow mein noodles ● Pickles

---

William Woodpecker
Use cream cheese to attach eyes and nose. With a table knife, make slits in the side of the zucchini and insert almonds.

1

2

Casper Caterpillar
Use a toothpick to poke two holes in the head, and insert the chow mein noodles for the antennae.

1

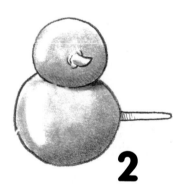

2

Eleanor Elephant
If you don't have zucchini, use a cucumber for the body and head.

1

2

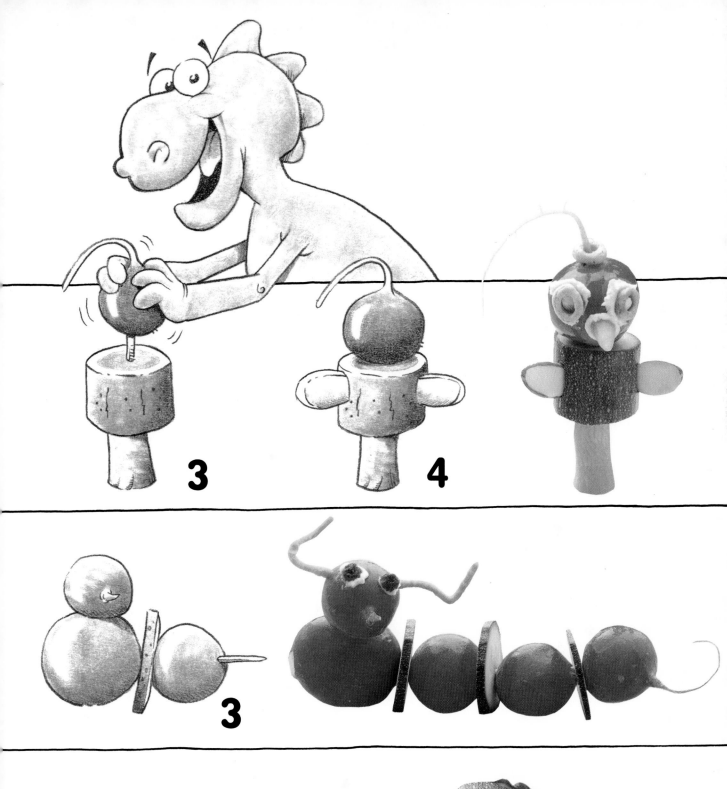

3

4

3

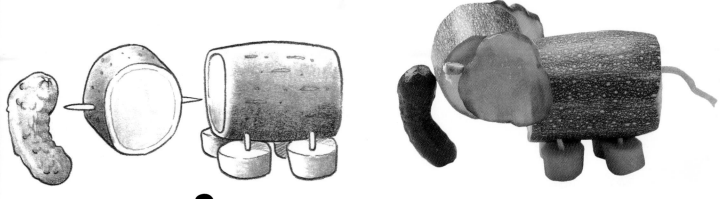

3

Identify lines and dots and which animals wear them.

Stripes and Spots

Did you know that stripes and spots
are lines and dots?

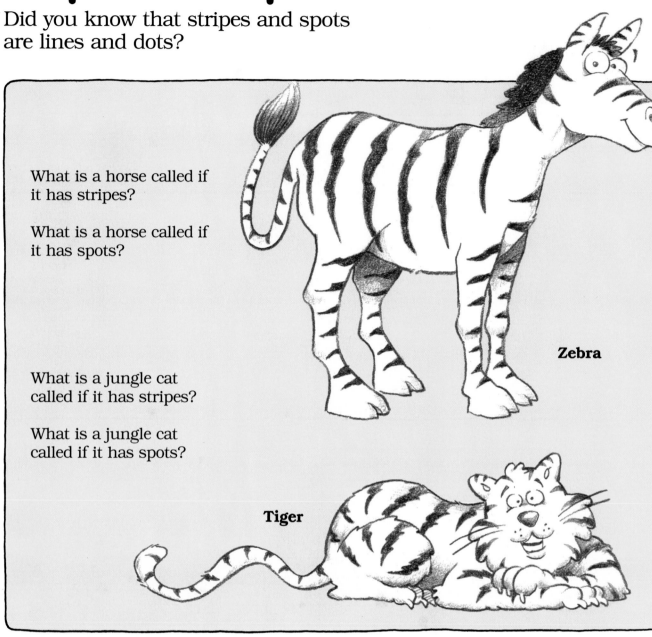

What is a horse called if
it has stripes?

What is a horse called if
it has spots?

What is a jungle cat
called if it has stripes?

What is a jungle cat
called if it has spots?

Zebra

Tiger

Which creatures below have stripes?
Which creatures below have spots?

Raccoon

Frog

Max

24

Pinto

Leopard

Fish

Bumblebee

Ladybug

Giraffe

Squish paint in paper for creative art.

Blob Globs

Dab blobs of paint onto paper and squish them together.
Presto! It's a Blob Glob with stripes and spots!

What you'll need...

- Newspapers or brown kraft paper
- Construction paper, halved crosswise
- Cotton swabs or paintbrushes
- Paints

1 Cover your work space with newspapers. Fold one piece of paper in half. Open it up and lay it flat. Using a cotton swab, dab different colors of paint onto half of the paper (see photo).

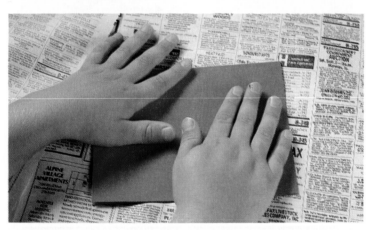

2 Fold the paper in half. Press paper firmly with your hands (see photo). This squishes the paint colors together.

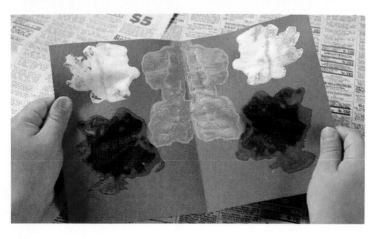

3 Open the paper up. Look at what you've made. Let your Blob Glob dry for about 1 hour.

Gobs of Fun

You can name them, give them to friends, cut them out, or hang them with a piece of yarn. What will you do with your Blob Glob? Aaron's Blob Glob looks like a butterfly. Natalie's looks like a leopard. What does your Blob Glob look like?

Decorate a lunch sack for a playful puppet.

Puppet Pals

Plain paper sacks are puppets just waiting to start talking.
Make a funny friend, and don't forget to add stripes or spots.

What you'll need...

- Scissors
- Small paper sack
- Construction paper or felt
- Tape
- Markers or crayons

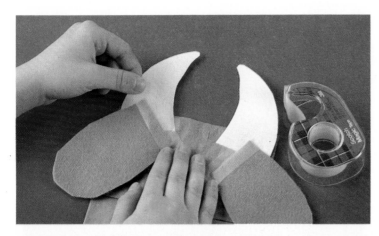

1 Cut shapes out of construction paper or felt for your puppet head. Tape the shapes to the sack (see photo).

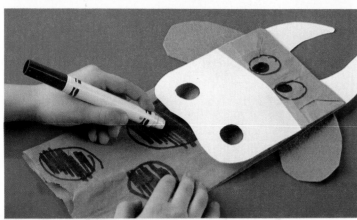

2 Draw stripes or spots on your Puppet Pal (see photo). Now put your hand inside the sack. Open and shut your hand to move your puppet's mouth.

Here are more puppet ideas.

Giraffe   **Raccoon**   **Frog**   **Bee**   **Cat**

We've filled this special section with more activities, recipes, reading suggestions, hints we learned from our kid-testers, and many other helpful tips.

Crazy Zoo Creatures

See pages 4 and 5

Visiting a zoo is a great way for children to see wild animals. Whether it's small or large, your local zoo is an exciting place for a family outing. In the meantime, look at Max's zoo with your children and talk about the animals that they can expect to see at a real zoo.

And Max's zoo has an added feature. All of the like animals are grouped together. Not only can your children count them, but they can *see* how many animals represent each number.

Thumbprint Critters

See pages 6 and 7

Our kid-testers gave us the "thumbs up" sign when they made these clever critters.

Some of their parents suggested making greeting cards for the holidays or personalized party invitations with their thumbprint critters.

Why stop with critters? Little thumbprints can become apples, flowers, pumpkins, beach balls, or even Easter eggs. Ask your children what else they can make with their thumbprints.

Eat-'Em-Up Animals

See pages 8 and 9

These edible bread-dough animals were a roaring success with our kid-testers. They liked creating their own creatures by squishing and pinching the dough together. Some kids made large dough creatures and others made baby dough creatures. Be sure to bake the large monsters made with lots of dough a few minutes longer than the smaller dough creatures.

Slithering Snakes

See pages 10 and 11

Our kid-testers all loved making their snakes slither by lifting them by their tongues. They giggled as the snakes uncoiled right before their eyes.

This project is easy for all children, but younger ones may need help drawing the spiral on the paper and cutting the snake out, especially if they use a paper plate.

Spiders, Spiders Everywhere

See pages 12 and 13

Spiders are amazing creatures. Children enjoy watching them in their homes. Help your child find a spiderweb by looking outside or in the corner of a basement. Lightly dust the web with white powder to help reveal all the intricate details.
- Reading suggestions:
The Very Busy Spider
   by Eric Carle
Spiders
   by Jane Dallinger
Spider Jane
   by Jane Yolen

Silly Pet Spider

See pages 14 and 15

If your children use plastic foam egg cups for their spiders, it is difficult to color the plastic with paint or water-soluble markers. Instead, let them use glue to decorate their Silly Pet Spiders. Our kid-testers used their imaginations and added glitter, pieces of construction paper, rickrack, lace, paper doilies, and sequins to their egg cups.

Spin a Spiderweb

See pages 16 and 17

The secret to making a sturdy twine spiderweb is to overlap the ends of the twine. This helps hold the web together when it dries. Our younger kid-testers needed some help with the overlapping.

If you want a colorful web, use yarn or embroidery floss. Let your children pick their favorite colors.

Sneak-a-Peek Garden

See pages 18 and 19

We all know that some kids turn their noses up at vegetables and fruits. Here are a few ways to serve these foods without children recognizing them.
● Add shredded carrot, zucchini, or apple to muffin and quick bread batter. Use about ½ cup shredded vegetable or fruit for 12 muffins or one loaf.
● Puree vegetable soup in a blender or food processor, making it creamy and disguising the vegetables.
● Sneak some cooked or finely shredded vegetables into tomato sauce and use it when you make pizza at home.
● Stir a few cooked or finely shredded vegetables into macaroni and cheese.
● Stir together cream cheese, fruit juice or milk, and finely chopped fruit to use as a tasty spread for toast or crackers.

Sweet Potato Partners

See pages 20 and 21

Are your children budding gardeners? Once they've mastered sweet potatoes, let them

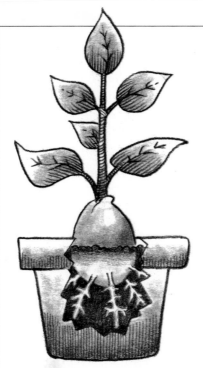

help sprout an avocado pit. Stick toothpicks in the pit and place it in a small jar of water. Make sure the rounded end of the pit is in the water. There should be enough water to cover the bottom half.

Place the jar in a sunny window. In a few weeks, sprouts will appear. Keep the pit watered, and your children can watch their garden grow. Once the pit sprouts leaves, plant it in a pot of dirt.

Crunchy Creatures

See pages 22 and 23

Our kid-testers were all giggles as they created their Crunchy Creatures. Before they started making their creatures, we patted the vegetables dry with a paper towel. This helped the cream cheese or peanut butter "glue" stick to the vegetables.

Set out a variety of materials and let your children create their own creatures. Help your children give their creatures funny names. Then ask your children questions like, What color is Casper Caterpillar? How many radishes did we use to make Casper? What did we use for William Woodpecker's nose? What is Eleanor Elephant's trunk made of? When your children are done playing with their creatures, they can nibble on them for a healthy snack.

Here's another idea for a Crunchy Creature. Stick 8 chow mein noodles into a cherry tomato. Stick on raisin eyes with cream cheese or peanut butter.

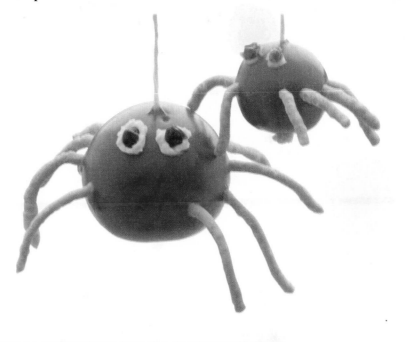

Stripes And Spots

See pages 24 and 25

Some creatures have both stripes and spots on their bodies. Can your children think of any of these creatures? Frogs, cats, and butterflies can have both stripes and spots.

Do your children know that some animals use their stripes for camouflage, and that other animals use them for recognition? A tiger's stripes help it blend in with tall grasses, making it hard to see the tiger. Then it can approach its prey unnoticed. On the other hand, zebras roam in open country, so their stripes aren't used for camouflage like a tiger's stripes. Instead, each zebra has its own unique stripes. That's how zebras recognize members of their own family.

Can your children find other creatures with stripes and spots somewhere else in the book? Start by looking on pages 4 and 5.

Blob Globs

See pages 26 and 27

Our kid-testers loved squishing the paper and paint together. But the fun didn't end there. They started imagining what their Blob Globs reminded them of. Then some of the children hung their creatures on hangers and made colorful Blob Glob mobiles to take home with them.

Puppet Pals

See pages 28 and 29

Before your children begin decorating their sacks, let them try the sacks on for size. If the sacks extend beyond their elbows, cut one to two inches off the bottom. Then it's easier for little arms and hands to move the puppets.

These little paper puppets really did live up to their names—they became our kid-testers' pals. Once the sacks were transformed into striped and spotted personalities, the kids had a friend for the day.

Cleanup Tips

When crafts and kids get together, it's time to take some precautions to help keep kids and their work area clean.
● Don't throw away your old shirts. Put them on your children before they begin painting or coloring with markers.
● Save old newspapers and spread them out over the children's work area. Keep the papers from sliding by taping them to the surface with masking tape.
● When children are painting, let them use cotton swabs instead of paintbrushes. Then when they finish their masterpieces, just throw the cotton swabs away.

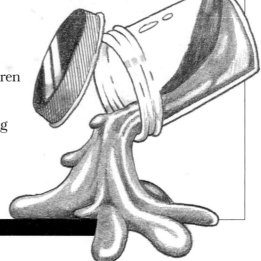

BETTER HOMES AND GARDENS ® BOOKS
Editor: Gerald M. Knox
Art Director: Ernest Shelton
Managing Editor: David Kirchner
Department Head, Food and Family Life: Sharyl Heiken

CRAZY CREATURES
Editors: Sandra Granseth and Linda Foley Woodrum
Editorial Project Manager: Rosanne Weber Mattson
Graphic Designers: Harjis Priekulis and Linda Ford Vermie
Contributing Illustrator: Buck Jones
Contributing Photographer: Scott Little

Have BETTER HOMES AND GARDENS ®
magazine delivered to your door.
For information, write to:
ROBERT AUSTIN
P.O. BOX 4536
DES MOINES, IA 50336